PUPPY POOL PARTY!

An **UNDERWATER DOGS** Adventure

To puppies everywhere and the kids who love them!

About This Book

The photographs in this book were taken with a digital SLR camera, with a fish-eye lens and flash, inside a special underwater casing designed for scuba divers. However, Seth did not use scuba diving breathing equipment, since he and the puppies were only underwater for a few seconds.

This book was edited by Leslie Shumate and designed by Phil Caminiti under the art direction of Saho Fujii. The text and display type were set in VAG rounded.

Photo Credits

Front cover (beach ball): popovaphoto/istockphoto.com • Back cover, 6–7, 36–37 (pool tile): Mauro_Scarone/istockphoto.com • 1, 4–5, 24, 30–31 (pool tile): BreatheFitness/istockphoto.com • 4 (beach ball): BreatheFitness/istockphoto.com • 8–9 (pool tile): zinchik/istockphoto.com • 10–11, 26–27, 40 (pool tile): Mercedes Rancaño Otero • 12–13, 35 (pool water): ermingut/istockphoto.com • 16–17 (pool tile): oleksagrzegorz/istockphoto.com • 18–19 (pool tile): Matthew71/istockphoto.com • 20–21 (pool water): webphotographeer/istockphoto.com • 22–23 (bubbles): Marat Sirotyukov/istockphoto.com • 28–29 (pool water): webphotographeer/istockphoto.com • 32–33 (pool water): LisaValder/istockphoto.com

First Scholastic printing, May 2017

Seth Casteel

PUPPY POOL PARTY!

An **UNDERWATER DOGS** Adventure

SCHOLASTIC INC.

YOU'RE INVITED

to a puppy pool party!

The sun is out. It's time to play.

Come swim and
splash the day away!

Test
the
water.

Dip
your
toes.

Blow some bubbles
through your nose!

Slip and slide.

Float and glide.

You're in for a fun wet ride!

**Run and jump.
Give it your all.**

You **splash** the most when you…

CANNONBALL!

Nice move, puppy! You've got style.

Now let's see your underwater smile.

Some pups paddle in a pair.

Swimming buddies love to share!

Safety first! It's crystal clear.

Don't swim without a lifeguard near.

Doggy-paddle,
strong and fast.

Swirling
bubbles
are a
BLAST!

Try the
deep end
when you're ready.

You can make it—slow and steady!

Crank the music.
Howl along.

Dance around to
your favorite song.

Swimming puppies
are so brave.

Surf's up, puppy!
Catch that wave.

If you're tired, take a break.

Dry off with a great big shake.

Warm and sleepy,

dream away.

What a fun
pool party day!

THE GUEST LIST

Orbit, 10 weeks

Hunter, 6 weeks

Cookie, 16 weeks

Avi, 5 months

Iggy, 15 weeks

Clyde, 16 weeks

Doc Brown, 9 weeks

McFly, 8 weeks

JR, 5 years

Buster, 6 years

Prince, 8 weeks

Jack, 12 weeks

Rocco, 5 years

Monty, 6 months

Flynn & Jenner, 3 years

Pringles & Pickme, 8 weeks

Grits & Reason, 12 weeks

Teenybopper, 7 weeks

Corey, 8 weeks

Caru, 6 weeks

Dora, 16 weeks

Atticus, 6 weeks

Simia, 9 weeks

Ruger, 7 weeks

Zelda, 8 weeks

Daisy, 5 years

Archie, 10 weeks

Pepper, 16 weeks

Ritzie, 9 weeks

Party Animal, 8 weeks

The Three Amigos, 8 weeks

Luna, 18 weeks

A NOTE FROM THE AUTHOR

To create these images, I taught swimming lessons to over 1,500 puppies, helping them to build confidence and safety skills in the water. Many of the youngest puppies only swam for a few minutes, but in that time they learned about buoyancy, their physicality in the water, and most importantly, how to get out of a pool. Some of the more adventurous puppies were instantly comfortable in the water and immediately began jumping in the pool and chasing toys! I'd like to give a big thank-you to all the amazing animal rescue organizations that helped to make this book possible by providing such wonderful puppies! Adoption is a great option!

Jackie Reich

Seth Casteel is an award-winning pet photographer and animal rights activist, as well as the bestselling author of *Underwater Dogs*, *Underwater Puppies*, and *Underwater Babies*. He lives in Los Angeles with his dog, Baby Nala.